the Corrs
unplugged

CW00410669

WISE PUBLICATIONS
London/New York/Sydney/Paris/Copenhagen/Madrid/Tokyo

Exclusive distributors:
Music Sales Limited
8/9 Frith Street, London W1V 5TZ, England.
Music Sales Pty Limited
120 Rothschild Avenue, Rosebery, NSW 2018, Australia.

Order No.AM962709
ISBN 0-7119-8036-5
This book © Copyright 1999 by Wise Publications.

Music arranged by Derek Jones.
Music engraved by Paul Ewers Music Design.

Printed in the United Kingdom by
Printwise (Haverhill) Limited, Haverhill, Suffolk.

Your Guarantee of Quality:
As publishers, we strive to produce every book to
the highest commercial standards.
The music has been freshly engraved and the book has
been carefully designed to minimise awkward page turns and
to make playing from it a real pleasure.
Particular care has been given to specifying acid-free,
neutral-sized paper made from pulps which have not been
elemental chlorine bleached.
This pulp is from farmed·sustainable forests and
was produced with special regard for the environment.
Throughout, the printing and binding have been planned to ensure
a sturdy, attractive publication which should give years of enjoyment.
If your copy fails to meet our high standards, please inform us
and we will gladly replace it.

Music Sales' complete catalogue describes thousands
of titles and is available in full colour sections by subject, direct
from Music Sales Limited.
Please state your areas of interest and send a cheque/postal order
for £1.50 for postage to: Music Sales Limited, Newmarket Road,
Bury St. Edmunds, Suffolk IP33 3YB.

www.musicsales.com

Only When I Sleep

Words & Music by Andrea Corr, Caroline Corr, Sharon Corr, Jim Corr,
John Shanks, Paul Peterson & Oliver Leiber

1. You're on - ly just a dream - boat, sail - ing in — my
2° sleep. — *(Verse 2 see block lyric)*

head. You swim my se - cret o - ceans of co - ral blue — and red. Your smell is in - cense burn-

It's reach-ing through— my skin, mov-ing from— with - in,— and clutch-es at— my breast.— But it's on - ly when I

Verse 2:

And when I wake from slumber
Your shadow's disappeared
Your breath is just a sea mist
Surrounding my body.
I'm working through the daytime
But when it's time to rest
I'm lying in my bed
Listening to my breath
Falling from the edge.

What Can I Do

Words & Music by Andrea Corr, Caroline Corr, Sharon Corr & Jim Corr

And I have been there ma - ny times

I just don't know what I'm do - ing wrong.

What can I do to make you love me?

What can I do to make you care?

What can I say___ to make___ you feel___ this?

4º To Coda ⊕ |1.

What can I do___ to get___ you there?___

Verse 2:
There's only so much I can take
And I just got to let it go.
And who knows I might feel better
If I don't try and I don't hope.

Verse 3:
Maybe there's nothing more to say
And in a funny way I'm calm.
Because the power is not mine
I'm just gonna let it fly.

Radio

Words & Music by Andrea Corr, Caroline Corr, Sharon Corr & Jim Corr

Verse 2:

Now it's morning light and it's cold outside
Caught up in a distant dream
I turn and think that you are by my side
So I leave my bed and I try to dress
Wondering why my mind plays tricks
And fools me in to thinking you are there
But you're just in my head
Swimming forever in my head
Not lying in my bed
Just swimming forever.

So listen to the radio *etc.*

Toss The Feathers

Traditional, arranged by Andrea Corr, Caroline Corr, Sharon Corr & Jim Corr

27

Runaway

Words & Music by Andrea Corr, Caroline Corr, Sharon Corr & Jim Corr

1. Say it's true,
(Verse 2 see block lyric)

there's no-thing like⎯⎯⎯ me and you.

you, no nev-er have,_____ I'm nev-er gon - na_____ stop fall - in' in love

with   you.

Violin

you,_____

with   you.

34

Verse 2:
Close the door, lay down upon the floor
And by candlelight make love to me through the night
Cos I have runaway
I have runaway, yeah, yeah
I have runaway, runaway
I have runaway with you.

Cos I have fallen in love, *etc.*

At Your Side

Words & Music by Andrea Corr, Caroline Corr, Sharon Corr & Jim Corr

Verse 2:
If life's standing still and your souls confused
And you cannot find what road to choose
If you make me stay you can't let me down
I will still believe I will turn around.

And you know that *etc.*

Forgiven Not Forgotten

Words & Music by Andrea Corr, Caroline Corr, Sharon Corr & Jim Corr

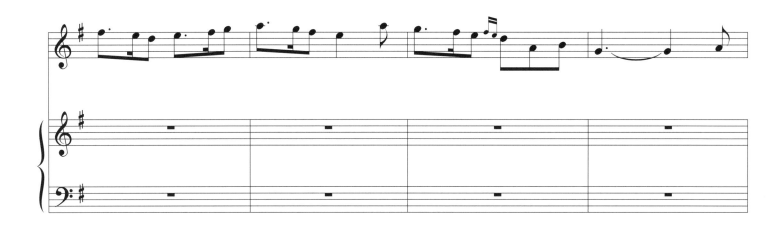

When her days are grey and her nights are black,
diff-er-ent shades of mun-dane, and the one-eyed fur-ry toy that
lies up-on the bed has of-ten heard her cry and heard her
whis-per out a name long for-giv-en, but not for-got-ten.

Still a-lone,_____ star-ing on,_____

wish-ing her life good-bye,_____ as she goes search-ing for the man__ long for-giv-

51

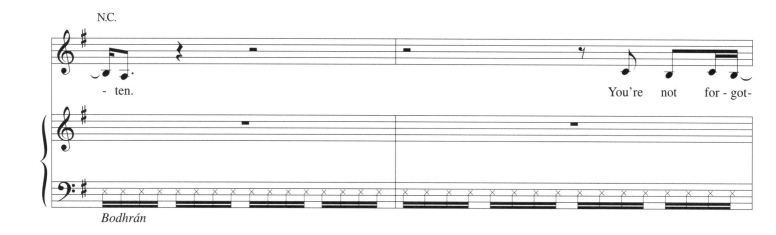

Verse 2:
A bleeding heart torn apart
And left on an icy grave
And a room where they once lay
Face to face
And nothing could get in their way
But now the memories of a man
Are haunting her days
And the craving never fades
She's still dreaming of a man.
Long forgiven
But not forgotten.

You're forgiven *etc.*

Little Wing

Words & Music by Jimi Hendrix

Violin & Whistle

a - ny - thing,_____

Violin & Whistle

Now she's

Violin & Whistle

Queen Of Hollywood

Words & Music by Andrea Corr, Caroline Corr, Sharon Corr, Jim Corr,
Glen Ballard, Dane DeViller & Sean Hosein.

1. She drove a long way through the night from an ur-ban neigh-bour-hood, she left her moth-er in a

(Verses 2, 3 & 4 see block lyric)

fight for a dream mis-un-der-stood, and her friends_ they talk on

it's a load-ed fan-ta-sy.

D.%. al Coda

Coda

No, she's nev-er gon-na be like the one be-fore,—— she read it in her

stars that there's some-thing more,___ no mat-ter what it takes, and ev-en though she

breaks, she'll be the queen of Hol-ly-wood. She is the queen of Hol-ly-

-wood, queen of Hol-ly-wood, and her friends still talk on

cor-ners.___

Verse 2:
But there was always something different
In the way she held a stare
And the pictures that she painted
Were of glamour and of flair.
And her boyfriend though he loved her
Knew he couldn't quite fulfil
He could never meet her there.

Verse 3:
And the cynics they will wonder
What's the difference with this dream
And the dreams of countless others
All believing in T.V.
They see their handprints in a sidewalk
Flashing cameras on the scene
And a shining limousine.

Verse 4:
Now her mother collects cut-outs
And the pictures make her smile
But if she saw behind the curtains
It could only make her cry.
She's got handprints on her body
Sad moonbeams in her eyes
Not so innocent a child.

Old Town

Words & Music by Phil Lynott & Jimmy Bain

1. The girl's a fool, she broke the rules, she hit him hard,
(Verse 2 see block lyric)

this time— he will break down.

She's lost his trust and so she must

This boy— has broke down.

Trumpet

This boy— is crack-ing up. This boy— has bro-
-ken down. This boy— is crack-ing up.
This boy— has broke down. I've been
spend-ing my mo-ney in the old town.— It's not the same, ho-ney, with

Verse 2:
She plays it hard, she plays it tough
But that's enough, the love is over
She's broke his heart and that is rough
But in the end he'll soon recover
The romance is over.

This boy is cracking up *etc.*

Lough Erin Shore

Traditional, arranged by Andrea Corr, Caroline Corr, Sharon Corr & Jim Corr

No Frontiers

Words & Music by Jimmy McCarthy

and if life— is a wild— wind———— that blows way— on high—

and your heart— is A-mel- lia dy- ing— to fly.—

Hea - ven— knows,——— no——— fron - tiers

and I've— seen— hea - ven in— your— eyes.—

Verse 2:
And if life is a rough bed of brambles and nails
And your spirit's slave to man's whips and man's jails
Where you thirst and you hunger for justice and right
And your heart is a pure flame of man's constant night.

In your eyes *etc.*

So Young

Words & Music by Andrea Corr, Caroline Corr, Sharon Corr & Jim Corr

Verse 2:
We are chasing the moon
Just running wild and free
We are following through
Every dream and every need.

And it really doesn't matter *etc.*